Quick Questions on Christianity

Dilwyn Hunt

RELIGIOUS AND MORAL EDUCATION PRESS

Published by Religious and Moral Education Press
A division of SCM-Canterbury Press Ltd
A wholly owned subsidiary of Hymns Ancient & Modern Ltd
St Mary's Works, St Mary's Plain
Norwich, Norfolk NR3 3BH

First published 1999

ISBN 1 85175 113 0

Designed by Topics – The Creative Partnership, Exeter

Printed in Great Britain by St Edmundsbury Press, Bury St Edmunds for SCM-Canterbury Press Ltd, Norwich

CONTENTS

This book was written with teachers in mind, particularly teachers of Religious Education, but it can be used by anybody who enjoys questions, quizzes, puzzles or games. From the point of view of Religious Education, the questions obviously have more to do with knowledge about Christianity than what can be learned from Christianity. Nevertheless, the questions can be used in many different ways to stimulate interest and make extending, reinforcing or revising knowledge about Christianity fun.

This book can provide questions for many popular types of quiz game involving either individuals or teams working co-operatively. For example, a particular section of the book could be a source of questions on a 'specialist subject' such as Christian festivals, or players could use it to prepare themselves to answer questions on this topic.

The questions can also be incorporated into board games or puzzles with a Christian theme. These could be devised by pupils or, for example, simply require players to answer questions on Christianity if they land on certain squares. The possibilities are almost endless.

1 Who was the first disciple to declare that Jesus was the Christ, the Son of the Living God?

2 What is the name of the Brazilian archbishop who said, 'When I give food to the poor, they call me a saint. When I ask why the poor have no food, they call me a communist'?

3 Which king of England in 1553 separated the Church of England from Rome?

4 The tomb of Archbishop Thomas à Becket, who was murdered in 1170, was once a major place of pilgrimage for European Christians. Where in Britain is it?

5 Who was the Roman governor who sentenced Jesus to be whipped and crucified?

6 In 1991 what European golf champion said, 'I think people who have ... millions of pounds or dollars or whatever, and all the sports cars and the homes and the places they want to go to, there's still something missing in their life. And I believe that's Jesus Christ'?

7 Name the town in Somerset where according to tradition Joseph of Arimathea preached the gospel. The town is also believed to have the ruins of the oldest monastery in England.

8 In 1873 the Christian priest Father Damien landed on the island of Molokai in order to fight what disease?

9 Who was given the Ten Commandments on Mount Sinai?

10 What was the name of the teenager from Lourdes who in 1858 believed she saw eighteen visions of the Blessed Virgin Mary?

QUESTIONS 1 – 10

PEOPLE AND PLACES

7

11 Who said, 'Love one another as I have loved you'?

12 Who took a boat to China in 1966 and today works with heroin addicts in Hong Kong, all of which she describes in her book *Chasing the Dragon* ?

13 What was the name of the German monk who in 1517 wrote ninety-five theses and so started the Protestant Reformation?

14 Some claim that the Church of the Holy Sepulchre marks the site where Jesus was placed in the tomb. In what city is it?

15 What is the river in which Jesus was baptized?

16 Michelangelo's painting of the 'Last Judgement' can be seen in the Sistine Chapel. In what building is the Sistine Chapel?

17 What is the name of the route through Jerusalem taken by Jesus to his execution on the cross?

18 What was the name of the disciple who betrayed Jesus?

19 What city in the south of France has a grotto and a spring of water which many Christians believe has the power to heal?

20 What do Christians believe happened at Golgotha, the place of the skulls?

QUESTIONS 11 – 20

21 The Church of the Nativity is said to mark the place where Jesus was born. In what city is it?

22 Vernie Bennett is a member of a female group who pray together before every show. What is the name of the group?

23 After caring for a two-year-old girl called Helen, Sister Frances Dominica was inspired to build the first what?

24 Who was the Christian youth club leader who said that she would trade in her MBE 'in exchange for a house to look after my foster-children'?

25 Following 'Inspiration Day' in 1946, Mother Teresa first began her work with the poor and sick in what city?

26 Who was the Scottish Christian missionary who was found in Africa by Sir Henry Stanley?

27 According to tradition, on what mountain was Jesus transfigured?

28 What nineteenth-century Quaker was outspoken in her demand for prison reform?

29 In Holland during the Second World War a woman risked her life and was eventually imprisoned in Ravensbruck concentration camp for hiding Jews from the Nazis. What was her name?

30 Shocked by the death and injury caused through war, Henry Dunant founded a Christian organization whose emblem was the same design but opposite colours of his nation's flag. What organization did he start?

PEOPLE AND PLACES

31 What sixth-century Christian, who later became Pope, said of British slaves, 'Not Angles but Angels'?

32 According to tradition, on what mountain did Noah's ark come to rest?

33 What was the name of the venerable eighth-century monk who wrote a history of the early Church in England?

34 What place of pilgrimage in Ireland did the Pope visit in 1979?

35 When he began his teaching ministry, around what lake did Jesus spend most of his time?

36 The Quaker William Penn founded a colony in North America and so began the 'Holy Experiment'. The city is named after him: what is it?

37 In what garden outside Jerusalem was Jesus arrested?

38 In the fourteenth century, who first translated the Latin New Testament into English?

39 Who was sent by the Pope as a missionary to England and became the first Archbishop of Canterbury in 597 CE?

40 Who was the sixteenth-century founder of the Scottish Presbyterian Church?

41 Geoffrey Chaucer wrote a collection of stories told by pilgrims going to what city?

42 What is the name of the small island in the Inner Hebrides where St Columba founded a monastery in 563 CE from which missionaries travelled to many places?

43 What is the name of the London home of the Archbishop of Canterbury?

44 For more than a thousand years no woman or female animal has been allowed to set foot on what Christian holy mountain?

45 What cardinal fell out of favour because he failed to persuade the Pope to grant Henry VIII a divorce from Catherine of Aragon?

46 Who was the sixteenth-century Spanish Carmelite nun who wrote *The Way of Perfection* and claimed to experience the presence of Jesus and moments of ecstasy?

47 What is the name of the Protestant community based near Cluny in France which undertakes evangelical work and also tries to promote unity amongst Christians?

48 Who is usually regarded as the first Christian martyr?

49 Every ten years a passion play recalling the last days of Jesus' life is performed in what town?

50 What was the name of the emperor who sought to blame the Christians for a fire which destroyed much of Rome in 64 CE?

51 Although he was not allowed to enter, who was permitted to see the Promised Land?

52 What seventh-century princess gave up her jewels to become abbess of Whitby monastery?

53 What was the name of the blind seventeenth-century Christian puritan who wrote 'Paradise Lost'?

54 Who is often called 'the lady with the lamp' as a result of her care for the dying and wounded during the Crimean War?

55 Following in the footsteps of Louis Pasteur, who was the Christian Quaker who pioneered 'antiseptic' surgery in Britain?

56 According to the Christian tradition, which disciple was crucified upside down in the city of Rome?

57 What was the name of the Norwegian bishop who organized resistance against the Nazis, by whom he was kept prisoner for three years, during the Second World War?

58 Pope John Paul died in 1978 after one of the shortest periods of office of any pope. For how many days was he pope?

59 Who as a young girl gave out coffee and sandwiches to down-and-outs in London and later wrote about her work in her book *Bury Me in My Boots*?

60 Often called the 'City of Peace', what city has been destroyed and rebuilt at least seven times throughout its long history?

61 Burnt at the stake as a witch by the English in 1431, who was declared to be a saint nearly five hundred years later?

62 Which of Jesus' twelve disciples is also the patron saint of Scotland?

63 Who was the nineteenth-century cardinal who explained why he left the Church of England to join the Roman Catholic Church in his book *Apologia pro Vita sua*?

64 The beautiful Church of St Sophia was once a mosque but now it is a museum. In what city is it?

65 Who was the Augustinian friar who edited the Great Bible of 1539 and spent most of his life fleeing from persecution?

66 Whose dying words included the request 'Father, forgive them for they know not what they do'?

67 Who was the black Victorian nurse who opened the 'British Hotel' in Sebastopol in which she provided shelter and care for soldiers wounded in the Crimean War?

68 In 1988 what British athlete said, 'I am going to the Olympic games because I'd love to be an Olympic champion, but that is not the only thing driving me. I'll do the best with the talent God has given me and hope he uses it to his glory, because it's not me, it's the Holy Spirit.'

69 Who was the English Catholic who was charged with treason and beheaded in 1535 when he refused to approve of Henry VIII's divorce and remarriage?

70 What was the first of its kind started by Robert Raikes in the eighteenth century that was opposed by some conservative Christians?

PEOPLE AND PLACES

71 What city is known as the 'Eternal City' whose bishops have become the supreme leader of the Catholic Church?

72 What is the name of the Christian preacher born in 1703 who covered thousands of miles travelling around Britain and who is reported to have said, 'The world is my parish'?

73 On Christmas Day 1066 William the Conqueror was crowned in which London abbey?

74 What sixteenth-century Protestant leader declared, 'I defy the Pope and his laws. If God spares my life, before many years I will cause a boy who drives the plough to know the Bible better than you do'?

75 What singer, who has the most number one hits, in 1969 gave the first of many concerts to support the Christian charity TEAR Fund?

76 Born in 480 CE, and sometimes known as the Father of Western Monasticism, who wrote a rule book for monastic life which is still the basis of monasticism today?

77 Awarded the OBE in 1971 and well known for his charity marathon runs, who has raised millions of pounds for Stoke Mandeville Hospital and for other good causes?

78 After the Exodus from Egypt what was the original name of the land that the Israelites settled in?

79 Crowned by Pope Leo III on Christmas Day 800 CE, who was the First Holy Roman Emperor?

80 Who is the patron saint of travellers, often shown as a strong man carrying Jesus as a child?

81 The crusaders massacred the Muslim and Jewish citizens when they captured what city in 1099 CE?

82 What is the small town in Portugal which has become a place of pilgrimage since three children claimed to have seen visions of 'Our Lady of the Rosary' there in 1917?

83 Who escaped from slavery in a southern state of America in 1849 but went back to lead over fifteen raids freeing more than three hundred slaves?

84 Who is the committed Christian who at the 1998 European Games won a gold medal in the triple jump?

85 Born in 1918 and author of The *Secret of Happiness*, who is the American Christian preacher who has led mass crusades to many countries?

86 Who was the Christian member of parliament who in 1807 managed to have the slave trade in Britain banned?

87 As the result of an eleventh-century vision, what place of pilgrimage in Norfolk has a replica of the Holy House of Nazareth?

88 What is the name of the French Protestant leader who in the sixteenth century virtually ruled Geneva?

89 Monks from Iona made their headquarters on what 'Holy Island' from where Christianity spread throughout Northumbria?

90 Who was born in the hillside town of Assisi and is said to have preached to the birds?

PEOPLE AND PLACES

BUILDINGS AND WORSHIP

91 At what ceremony do godparents promise that a child will be brought up in the Christian faith?

92 What is the name of the reading stand from which the Bible is read in many churches?

93 Every diocese has a main church sometimes called the bishop's church. By what other name are these churches known?

94 Many Christians believe that they receive the body and blood of Christ during what act of worship?

95 What is the name given to a painting or carving that represents the figure of Jesus on the cross?

96 Traditionally speakers often stand on a raised platform when giving a sermon in a church. What is it called?

97 What is the shepherd's crook called which a bishop carries as a symbol of being a Good Shepherd?

98 What is the name of the screen used in an Orthodox church to separate the sanctuary from the nave?

99 What Christian prayer begins with the words 'Our Father, which art in heaven'?

100 What branch of Christianity has a 'corps cadet brigade' for its youth members who wish to take up serious training?

QUESTIONS 91 – 100

101 What branch of Christianity, started in the seventeenth century, doesn't baptize infants but instead has adult or believer's baptism?

102 Margaret Thatcher was quoting the prayer of what thirteenth-century saint when she said, 'Lord, make me an instrument of thy peace. Where there is hatred let me sow love'?

103 What flat-topped piece of church furniture usually has candles, a cross and bread and wine placed on it during the Eucharist?

104 As a follow-up to baptism in some branches of the Church, what ritual enters a person into full membership of the Christian Church?

105 Used during the service of Eucharist or Holy Communion, what is the host?

106 Many church buildings have projecting stone waterspouts which are often in the shape of ugly animals or demons. What are these waterspouts called?

107 When a Christian priest says that a person has been forgiven for their sins, what is this called?

108 What book contains the words of the Roman Catholic Mass?

109 In what branch of Christianity do worshippers stand throughout the services?

110 What is a roofed gateway into a churchyard called?

BUILDINGS AND WORSHIP

111 What is the speech or homily called which forms an important part of many church services?

112 Arranging seats into a circle, sitting in silence and awaiting the coming of the Spirit is a form of worship used in what branch of Christianity?

113 In a church service what happens at the offertory?

114 What is the long black gown often worn by Christian priests during church services and also sometimes for day-to-day use?

115 What are prayers called where the worshipper asks for God's help in dealing with their personal desires and needs?

116 What Hebrew word, which means something like 'so be it' or 'we all agree', is often used to end prayer?

117 In some churches a heated metal container filled with incense is swung to and fro on chains. What is the metal container called?

118 What large keyboard instrument is often used to provide music in a church?

119 What is the name given to the room in a church tower in which the bells are hung?

120 Who designed St Paul's Cathedral in London?

121 What is the name for the ceremonial clothing and symbols worn by the clergy during church services?

122 Often made of silver, what is the cup or goblet called which is used to hold the communion wine in many churches?

123 During what Christian ceremony would you hear the words 'till death us do part'?

124 The Paternoster, meaning 'Our Father', is the Latin name for what Christian prayer?

125 At what time of day does the Christian service of Matins take place?

126 Who was the famous eighteenth-century English preacher who composed over five thousand hymns, including 'Hark, the herald angels sing', and who had a famous brother called John?

127 What is the name of the plate, usually made of silver, on which communion bread is placed?

128 What is the name of the ritual which marks a person's appointment as a priest?

129 In what branch of Christianity are leaders called 'officers' and members called 'soldiers'?

130 What church stands on top of Vatican Hill at the end of a large square known as Piazza San Pietro?

131 Many churches have fixed benches on which people sit. What are these benches called?

132 What is the name of the small room in a church used by ministers to put on their robes?

133 During christening a person is given a 'Christian' name. By what other name is this ritual known?

134 In a church what is the name given to an enclosed area in which a priest listens to a person admit their sins.

135 Some churches are decorated with pictures produced by painting on fresh plaster. What is such a painting called?

136 Many Christians say a prayer before eating food. What are these prayers called?

137 The Salvation Army does not have any sacraments. What other large branch of Christianity has no sacraments?

138 During Eucharist or Holy Communion what is used as a symbol of the blood of Christ?

139 Often made of stone with eight sides, what piece of church furniture is used during baptism?

140 In the preface to its hymn book what branch of Christianity describes itself as 'born in song'?

141 During what Christian ceremony would you hear the words, 'earth to earth, ashes to ashes, dust to dust'?

142 As a symbol that he or she represents Jesus, a priest sometimes wears a long white gown. What is this gown called?

143 In a Methodist church there is a table which serves as a reminder of the table around which Jesus and the disciples sat for the Last Supper. What is this table called?

144 In Christianity a sick or dying person may be anointed with oil by a priest. What is this practice called?

145 What is the name of the raised area immediately around the altar and behind the altar-rail?

146 In the Anglican Church following this ceremony, which involves the laying on of hands by a bishop, a person can receive the bread and wine at Eucharist. What is the ceremony called?

147 What branch of Christianity traditionally holds meetings out of doors or in halls called citadels?

148 During baptism of a child, who, in the event of the death of its parents, undertakes responsibility for the spiritual welfare of the newly baptized youngster?

149 What name was given to the inner sanctuary in the Jerusalem Temple into which only the High Priest was permitted to enter?

150 What is the name of the set of 165 beads plus a crucifix that is used by some Christians for worship?

151 Many priests wear a garment which is made of silk and is about two and a half metres long and about ten centimetres wide. What is it called?

152 A verger traditionally leads a church procession carrying a mace. What is the mace called?

153 In a traditional church the worshippers usually face in what compass direction?

154 During what Christian ceremony would a person be sprinkled or sometimes covered with water?

155 What is the other name for the service called Evening Prayer which is found in the Anglican Prayer Book?

156 What piece of church furniture is often in the shape of an eagle standing on a globe?

157 Which English cathedral was bombed in 1940 and was rebuilt as a new cathedral alongside the ruins of the old?

158 Often based on biblical texts, what are the religious songs sung in a church?

159 The Roman Catholic Church has seven central rituals – baptism, confirmation, confession, ordination, marriage, mass and unction. What are these rituals called?

160 During what ceremony would you hear the words 'Take, eat, this is my Body which is given for you'?

161 In the precincts of what building was Jesus when he upset the tables of the money-changers and the seats of the dealers in pigeons?

162 What Bible character built an ark to save his family and the animals from a flood?

163 He became a good and loyal disciple, but before he met Jesus he worked for the Romans as a tax-collector. Who was he?

164 What Bible character ran away from God's command and ended up in the belly of a big fish?

165 Luke, John and Matthew were three of the Gospel writers. Name the other one.

166 Who was the rich tax-collector who climbed a tree to see Jesus and after meeting him repaid money he had taken from others?

167 Who was the wicked wife of King Ahab who tried to replace the worship of God with the god Baal?

168 Jacob had twelve sons. Which one was his favourite?

169 In the Bible who was married to Sarah and later Hagar and received the first covenant promise from God?

170 While her sister Mary sat at Jesus' feet who busied herself preparing food?

THE BIBLE

THE BIBLE

171 A man who is wounded by thieves is helped by a stranger. What is this Bible parable called?

172 In the account of his baptism, as a symbol of the Holy Spirit, what appears above Jesus' head?

173 Who was the great thinker and preacher of Christianity who wrote in one of his letters, 'Love bears all things, believes all things, hopes all things, endures all things'?

174 In the Bible story about the sons of Adam and Eve, who killed Abel and afterwards asked, 'Am I my brother's keeper?'?

175 In the Bible story what food did Jesus give to the crowd of five thousand which left them all satisfied?

176 Which book in the Bible begins with the words 'In the beginning God created the heavens and the earth'?

177 What Bible character killed the giant Goliath and went on to become king of Israel?

178 In the story of the Burning Bush, who did God command to return to Egypt to free the Hebrew slaves?

179 Who was the strong man who, the Bible tells us, lost his strength when his hair was cut?

180 One of the great teachers of Christianity, his vision on the road to Damascus is described in the Bible. Who was he?

181 What is the collection of twenty-seven books that form the main Christian scriptures?

182 In the Bible story who led the Hebrew people across the Red Sea?

183 In the Bible story of the Creation and the Fall who was the woman who was tempted by the snake?

184 Refusing to give up his faith, what Bible character was imprisoned in a den of lions?

185 Which of Jesus' disciples escaped from King Herod's prison with the help of an angel?

186 In the Bible story Jesus prevented a woman from being stoned to death. What was she accused of?

187 Who in the Bible had a coat of many colours?

188 In the Bible story what was the image the Hebrews made and worshipped while they were at the foot of Mount Sinai?

189 In the Bible story, as well as quails what other food did God provide for Moses and the Hebrew people while they were in the wilderness?

190 What is the name given to the early Israelite leaders such as Abraham, Isaac and Jacob?

THE BIBLE

191 In the New Testament there are a number of epistles written by Paul of Tarsus. What is an epistle?

192 At a marriage in Cana, according to the Bible story, what miracle did Jesus perform?

193 Which Gospel begins with the words 'In the beginning was the Word, and the Word was with God, and the Word was God'?

194 What was the name of the king who saw the writing on the wall?

195 According to the Bible story, who was the woman who first saw the resurrected Jesus?

196 The Latin translation of the Bible is known as the 'Vulgate'. Who first translated the Bible into Latin?

197 What is the name given to the stories told by Jesus which have a moral or religious message?

198 What version of the English Bible was first published in 1611 during the reign of James I and is still considered by some Christians to be the most beautiful and dignified English translation?

199 Jesus began the Sermon on the Mount with nine sayings each beginning with the word 'Blessed'. What are these nine sayings called?

200 Mary is the mother of Jesus. What was the name of her relative who was the mother of John the Baptist?

201 Who was the fourth Israelite judge who in the Bible story refused to be king, saying, 'The Lord shall rule over you'?

202 Said to have lived to nine hundred and sixty-nine years, who is the oldest person mentioned in the Bible?

203 Who was the disciple who doubted that Jesus had risen from the dead?

204 After the rain had stopped which was the first bird Noah released from the ark?

205 While on the island of Patmos who is said to have received the Revelation, the last book in the New Testament?

206 In the Bible story what was the name of Uriah's wife whom King David took a particular liking for and later on married?

207 In the Bible wise men brought three gifts for the baby Jesus. Gold and frankincense were two. What was the third gift?

208 'The Lord is my shepherd; I shall not want. He makes me lie down in green pastures: he leads me beside still waters.' In what book of the Bible are these words found?

209 The Bible contains the Decalogue which is a list of rules said to have been given to Moses and written on two tablets of stone. By what other name is the Decalogue more widely known?

210 In the Bible story, when he was near Jericho Jesus cured a man called Bartimaeus. What did Bartimaeus suffer from?

211 According to the Bible story, on the evening of his resurrection, in what village did Jesus appear to two of his disciples?

212 In the Bible who was the female Israelite judge who led her people to victory over the Canaanites?

213 According to Luke's Gospel who was the Roman Emperor when Jesus was born?

214 Who was the Christian physician who wrote the Acts of the Apostles and the third Gospel?

215 Who was the sister of Martha who sat at Jesus' feet while Martha was busy preparing a meal?

216 Which Gospel begins with the story of John the Baptist?

217 As a sign of the covenant promise between God and all humankind what did God show Noah?

218 What is the name of the glorious vision, described in the New Testament, when Jesus appeared with Moses and Elijah?

219 At Caesarea Philippi who told Jesus, 'You are the Christ'?

220 After his baptism Jesus went into the wilderness where he was tempted by the devil. For how many days and nights was he in the wilderness?

PEOPLE AND PLACES

Page 7

1. Peter (Simon)
2. Helder Camara
3. Henry VIII
4. Canterbury Cathedral
5. Pontius Pilate
6. Bernhard Langer
7. Glastonbury
8. Leprosy
9. Moses
10. Bernadette Soubirous

Page 8

11. Jesus
12. Jackie Pullinger
13. Martin Luther
14. Jerusalem
15. River Jordan
16. The Vatican
17. Via Dolorosa
18. Judas Iscariot
19. Lourdes
20. Jesus' crucifixion

Page 9

21. Bethlehem
22. Eternal

23. Children's hospice
24. Sybil Phoenix
25. Calcutta
26. David Livingstone
27. Mount Tabor
28. Elizabeth Fry
29. Corrie ten Boom
30. The Red Cross

Page 10

31. Gregory the Great
32. Mount Ararat
33. The Venerable Bede
34. Knock
35. Lake Galilee
36. Pennsylvania
37. Gethsemane
38. John Wycliffe
39. Augustine of Canterbury
40. John Knox

Page 11

41. Canterbury
42. Iona
43. The Palace of Lambeth
44. Mount Athos
45. Thomas Wolsey

46. St Teresa of Avila
47. Taizé
48. St Stephen
49. Oberammergau
50. Nero

Page 12

51. Moses
52. Hilda
53. John Milton
54. Florence Nightingale
55. Joseph Lister
56. Peter (Simon)
57. Eivind Berggrav
58. Thirty-three days
59. Sally Trench
60. Jerusalem

Page 13

61. Joan of Arc
62. St Andrew
63. John Henry Newman
64. Istanbul
65. Miles Coverdale
66. Jesus
67. Mary Seacole
68. Kriss Akabusi
69. Thomas More
70. Sunday School

ANSWERS 1 – 70

ANSWERS

Page 14

71. Rome
72. John Wesley
73. Westminster Abbey
74. William Tyndale
75. Cliff Richard
76. St Benedict
77. Jimmy Saville
78. Canaan
79. Charlemagne
80. St Christopher

Page 15

81. Jerusalem
82. Fatima
83. Harriet Tubman
84. Jonathan Edwards
85. Billy Graham
86. William Wilberforce
87. Walsingham
88. John Calvin
89. Lindisfarne
90. St Francis

BUILDINGS AND WORSHIP

Page 16

91. Baptism (christening)
92. A lectern
93. A cathedral

94. Eucharist (Holy Communion, Mass)
95. A crucifix
96. A pulpit
97. A crozier
98. An iconostasis
99. The Lord's Prayer
100. The Salvation Army

Page 17

101. The Baptists
102. St Francis of Assisi
103. The altar (communion table)
104. Confirmation
105. Consecrated bread
106. Gargoyles
107. Absolution
108. The Missal
109. Orthodox
110. A lych-gate

Page 18

111. A sermon
112. Society of Friends (Quakers)
113. A collection of money
114. A cassock
115. Petition
116. Amen
117. A thurible (censer)

118. An organ
119. A belfry
120. Sir Christopher Wren

Page 19

121. Vestments
122. The chalice
123. A marriage ceremony
124. The Lord's Prayer
125. Morning
126. Charles Wesley
127. A paten
128. Ordination
129. The Salvation Army
130. St Peter's Church

Page 20

131. Pews
132. The vestry
133. Baptism
134. A confessional
135. A fresco
136. Grace
137. The Society of Friends (Quakers)
138. Wine
139. A font
140. The Methodist Church

Page 21

141. A funeral
142. An alb
143. A communion table
144. Unction (extreme unction, chrism)
145. The sanctuary
146. Confirmation
147. The Salvation Army
148. Godparents
149. The Holy of Holies
150. A rosary

Page 22

151. A stole
152. A verge
153. East
154. Baptism
155. Evensong
156. A lectern
157. Coventry Cathedral
158. Hymns
159. The sacraments
160. Eucharist (Holy Communion, Mass)

THE BIBLE

Page 23

161. The Jerusalem Temple
162. Noah
163. Matthew (Levi)
164. Jonah
165. Mark
166. Zacchaeus
167. Jezebel
168. Joseph
169. Abraham
170. Martha

Page 24

171. The Good Samaritan
172. A dove
173. Paul of Tarsus (St Paul)
174. Cain
175. Five loaves and two fishes
176. Genesis
177. David
178. Moses
179. Samson
180. Paul of Tarsus (St Paul, Saul)

Page 25

181. The New Testament
182. Moses
183. Eve
184. Daniel
185. Peter (Simon)
186. Adultery
187. Joseph
188. A golden calf
189. Manna
190. The Patriarchs

Page 26

191. A letter
192. Turning water into wine
193. John's Gospel
194. Belshazzar
195. Mary Magdalene
196. St Jerome
197. Parables
198. The Authorized Version, King James' Version
199. The Beatitudes
200. Elizabeth

Page 27

201. Gideon
202. Methuselah
203. Thomas
204. A raven
205. St John the Divine
206. Bathsheba
207. Myrrh
208. The Psalms
209. The Ten Commandments
210. Blindness

ANSWERS

Page 28

211. Emmaus
212. Deborah
213. Emperor Augustus
214. Luke
215. Mary of Bethany
216. Mark's Gospel
217. A rainbow
218. The Transfiguration
219. Peter (Simon)
220. Forty

Page 37

221. Jacob
222. Ruth
223. The Evangelion (Book of the Gospels)
224. Pontius Pilate
225. Acts of the Apostles
226. Garden of Eden
227. Caiaphas
228. Good news
229. A dove
230. Elijah

Page 38

231. The Book of Kells
232. Mark's Gospel
233. Rested

234. The elder son
235. Lot's wife
236. Twelve
237. Moses
238. John the Baptist
239. A camel
240. Gomorrah

Page 39

241. Anger (wrath)
242. A tower
243. Delilah
244. Lazarus
245. Revelation
246. Ten
247. Peter (Simon)
248. Thirty
249. Job
250. Queen Esther

FASTS AND FESTIVALS

Page 40

251. Maundy Thursday
252. Advent
253. Palm Sunday
254. Ascension
255. Ash Wednesday
256. Easter Sunday
257. Whitsun (Pentecost)

258. Jesus
259. Trinity Sunday
260. Pancakes

Page 41

261. Lent
262. Ash Wednesday
263. Christmas
264. Maundy Thursday
265. Good Friday
266. Easter Sunday
267. Christmas
268. Corpus Christi
269. Epiphany
270. Whitsun (Pentecost)

Page 42

271. Good Friday
272. A crown of candles
273. Christmas
274. Palm Sunday
275. Easter Sunday
276. Easter
277. The Assumption of the Blessed Virgin Mary
278. Advent
279. Mothering Sunday
280. Trinity Sunday

Page 43

281. Mistletoe
282. Easter Sunday
283. A Christmas card
284. Simnel cake
285. 1st November
286. Boxing Day
287. Thanksgiving
288. Good Friday
289. St Nicholas
290. Mardi Gras

Page 44

291. A pancake race
292. The Pope
293. 26th December
294. Candlemas
295. 'Farewell to meat'
296. Lent
297. Shrove Tuesday
298. Michaelmas
299. King Wenceslas
300. Ascension Day

Page 45

301. A paschal candle
302. Christmas
303. Maundy Thursday

304. Candlemas
305. The Christmas tree
306. Good Friday
307. The day after Good Friday (the day before Easter Sunday)
308. Whitsun (Pentecost)
309. Orthodox Christianity
310. An advent calendar

Page 46

311. Lent
312. Whitsun (Pentecost)
313. Easter Sunday
314. Tuesday
315. Maundy Thursday
316. Good Friday
317. Ascension Day
318. Christmas
319. Whitsun (Pentecost)
320. Harvest

Page 47

321. Christmas
322. Mothering Sunday

323. Hot-cross buns
324. Maundy Thursday
325. St Valentine's Day
326. An orange
327. Harvest
328. Holly
329. Judas Iscariot
330. Thursday

BELIEFS

Page 48

331. A virgin birth
332. The Creed
333. Purgatory
334. The Roman Catholic Church
335. He rose from the dead.
336. Pacifism
337. An atheist
338. Sunday
339. Euthanasia
340. Honour your father and your mother.

Page 49

341. Vivisection
342. Desmond Tutu

ANSWERS

343. Heaven (paradise)

344. Monotheism

345. A saint

346. The Holy Spirit

347. The Messiah

348. Jesus

349. Seven

350. The Apostles' Creed

Page 50

351. Jesus

352. The Virgin Mary (Mary, the mother of Jesus)

353. Peter (Simon)

354. Jesus

355. Hell (Hades, Gehenna)

356. Predestination

357. Transubstantiation

358. Blasphemy

359. The Holy Grail

360. Seventh Day Adventists

Page 51

361. Friday

362. The Immaculate Conception

363. Satan (the devil, Lucifer)

364. Armageddon

365. Death

366. Galileo

367. An icon

368. Jesus

369. An agnostic

370. The Virgin Mary (Mary, the mother of Jesus)

Page 52

371. The Creed

372. Original sin

373. The Trinity

374. Jesus

375. Drink alcohol

376. Jesus

377. All-powerful

378. Baptism

379. The Roman Catholic Church

380. The Virgin Mary (Mary, the mother of Jesus)

Page 53

381. Satan (the devil)

382. Abortion

383. Angels

384. Charles Darwin

385. Jesus

386. The Virgin Mary (Mary, the mother of Jesus)

387. The Roman Catholic Church

388. Jesus

389. A miracle

390. Monogamy

Page 54

391. Living without sex, remaining unmarried

392. Mother Teresa

393. Soul or spirit

394. The Golden Rule

395. An idol

396. The Trinity

397. Latin America (South America)

398. Belief in more than one god

399. Pope John Paul II

400. The Society of Friends (Quakers)

GENERAL

Page 55

401. Thomas Cranmer
402. Pope John XXIII
403. The Samaritans
404. The Inquisition
405. The Salvation Army
406. Gladys Aylward
407. Abortion
408. Thomas Barnardo
409. St George
410. Albert Schweitzer

Page 56

411. Desmond Tutu
412. Dietrich Bonhoeffer
413. Leprosy
414. William Tyndale
415. Mother Teresa
416. George Fox
417. Lord Shaftesbury
418. St Alban
419. John Wesley
420. Leonard Cheshire

Page 57

421. Terry Waite
422. Martin Luther King

423. The Pope
424. The Salvation Army
425. Cliff Richard
426. Constantine
427. Thomas More
428. St Ignatius Loyola
429. Ecumenism (Oikoumene)
430. *The Pilgrim's Progress*

Page 58

431. A fish
432. The Roman Catholic Church
433. Anno Domini (in the year of Our Lord)
434. The Church of England
435. Torture, killed by lions and other wild animals
436. The Hospice Movement
437. Christian Aid
438. The beginning and the end (God and Jesus)
439. David Jenkins (the Bishop of Durham)
440. Speaking in tongues

Page 59

441. St Augustine of Hippo
442. The Apostles
443. The laity (lay people)
444. Cardinals
445. John Wycliffe
446. Martin Luther
447. Stigmata
448. The World Council of Churches
449. The Pope
450. The Archbishop of York

Page 60

451. The Methodist Church
452. Thomas Aquinas
453. CAFOD
454. Oscar Romero
455. Aslan, the lion
456. Trevor Huddleston
457. Catechism
458. John Wycliffe
459. Paul of Tarsus (St Paul)
460. The Bartholomew's Day Massacre

ANSWERS

Page 61

461. William Carey
462. Constantine
463. Eastern Orthodox
464. Mary Slessor
465. John F. Kennedy
466. Peter (Simon)
467. Sloth
468. Canonization
469. May
470. Apartheid

Page 62

471. A bishop (archbishop, abbot)
472. The Church of England
473. A tonsure
474. Thirty Years' War
475. Prince Charles
476. Ebenezer Scrooge
477. Mother Teresa of Calcutta
478. A lion
479. Nuclear weapons
480. Polish

Page 63

481. Rings
482. The United Reformed Church
483. Paul of Tarsus (St Paul)
484. Number of divorces
485. A crown of thorns
486. *Songs of Praise*
487. 1967
488. The altar (communion table)
489. The Angel Gabriel
490. God the Father

Page 64

491. The Holy Shroud
492. The Orthodox Church
493. Fourteen
494. Jesus
495. *The Witness*
496. Archbishop of Canterbury
497. The World Council of Churches
498. A halo
499. The Hail Mary (Ave Maria)
500. William Booth

221 In the Bible story who, in a dream, saw a ladder reaching up into heaven?

222 She was a woman from Moab, friend of Naomi, and great grand-mother of King David. Who was she?

223 In an Orthodox church what is the special book called which is carried in procession and is often decorated with silver and gold?

224 In the Bible story who washed his hands, saying about Jesus, 'I am innocent of this man's blood'?

225 What book in the New Testament tells the story of the missionary journeys of St Paul?

226 What is the name of the idyllic garden in which Adam and Eve were first placed by God?

227 According to Matthew's Gospel what was the name of the high priest who led Jesus' first trial and who demanded that Jesus should be sentenced to death?

228 What does the word 'gospel' mean?

229 Used widely as a symbol of peace, in the story of Noah what animal brought an olive branch back to the ark?

230 In the Bible who was the prophet who fought against the introduction of the worship of Baal by King Ahab and Queen Jezebel?

THE BIBLE

THE BIBLE

231 What is the name of the famous eighth-century, beautifully ornamented Bible which was produced in a monastery in Ireland?

232 Which is the shortest Gospel in the New Testament?

233 In the Bible story of creation what did God do on the seventh day?

234 In Jesus' story about a forgiving father and a prodigal son, who became angry and refused to join the celebration?

235 In the Bible story who looked back and was turned into a pillar of salt?

236 According to the Bible story how many tribes of Israel were there?

237 Who in the Bible was told to remove his shoes because he was on holy ground?

238 Who in the Bible was clothed in camel's hair and ate locusts and wild honey?

239 Jesus once said that it was easier for what animal to go through the eye of a needle than for a rich man to enter the kingdom of God?

240 In the Bible God ordered that two evil cities should be destroyed. One was Sodom. What was the name of the other city?

THE BIBLE

Quick Questions on Christianity

241 According to one of the proverbs in the Bible, a soft answer turns away what?

242 In the Bible story what did the people of Babel build?

243 Who was the beautiful woman who tricked Samson and robbed him of his strength?

244 Who was the brother of Mary and Martha whom Jesus brought back to life?

245 In what book in the Bible is there a vision of the holy city coming down out of heaven?

246 Because the Pharaoh wouldn't let the slaves go, how many plagues did the Egyptians suffer?

247 James and John were two of the disciples with Jesus during his transfiguration. Who was the third disciple?

248 How many pieces of silver did Judas Iscariot receive for betraying Jesus?

249 Who in the Bible was the blameless and upright man who is famous for having suffered much?

250 Who was the queen of Persia who uncovered Haman's plot and saved the Jewish people from destruction?

QUESTIONS 241 – 250

THE BIBLE

39

FASTS AND FESTIVALS

251 On what Christian festival day is it traditional in Britain for the queen or king to give away special coins?

252 What festival, usually lasting about twenty-four days, provides a preparation for Christmas?

253 On what festival day do Christians recall the story of Jesus entering Jerusalem riding on a donkey?

254 What Christian festival, forty days after Easter, celebrates the story of the risen Jesus leaving earth and being enthroned in heaven?

255 On what day does Lent begin?

256 Chocolate eggs are eaten on what festival day?

257 What festival is celebrated fifty days after Easter?

258 During Holy Week Christians recall the last week of whose life?

259 Which Christian festival is often an occasion for the ordination of priests?

260 What special food is traditionally eaten on Shrove Tuesday?

261 The Bible records the story of Jesus' temptation in the wilderness for forty days and nights. During what period in the Christian year is this recalled?

262 On what festival day is it traditional for Christians to receive a cross of ashes marked on their forehead?

263 A crib scene containing the figures of Mary and Joseph will often be made during what Christian festival?

264 On what festival day do Christians recall the story of Jesus washing the feet of his disciples?

265 In Orthodox churches on what day is a cloth bearing the image of the dead Jesus carried in procession around the church?

266 Some Christians take part in a midnight procession around their church and then in the early hours of the next morning they enter the church and announce, 'Christ is risen'. What festival day is this?

267 During which Christian festival do people try to forget old quarrels, give presents and possibly go to a midnight mass?

268 What Christian festival is celebrated by a procession in which consecrated bread is carried in a container?

269 What festival takes place on the 6th of January and celebrates the visit of the wise men to see the child Jesus?

270 Because it is associated with the Holy Spirit, what Christian festival was once a popular time for new members to join the Church through baptism?

FASTS AND FESTIVALS

271 Hot cross buns are eaten on what Christian festival day?

272 On December 13th some Christians celebrate the story of Lucia, a girl who carried food to the persecuted Christians hiding in the catacombs underneath Rome. During the celebration what do St Lucia girls today wear on their heads?

273 What Christian festival is celebrated by singing carols and sending cards to friends and family?

274 On what day may Christians receive pieces of palm leaf in the form of a cross?

275 A large paschal candle is carried through a church on what special day?

276 What festival is thought to be named after the goddess of spring who is sometimes called Ostara or Osterr?

277 What festival celebrates the Roman Catholic teaching that when Mary, Jesus' mother, died, she was taken body and soul into heaven?

278 The Christian Church year begins on the Sunday nearest St Andrew's Day. What is the start of the Church year called?

279 Refreshment Sunday, or the fourth Sunday in Lent, is more widely known as what?

280 What festival takes place on the Sunday after Whitsun and celebrates the Christian belief in God as Father, Son and Holy Spirit?

QUESTIONS 271 – 280

281 Once venerated by the Druids because it was rare, what plant is often hung above doorways in homes where Christmas is celebrated?

282 Rolling eggs, cracking eggs and decorating eggs are all customs associated with what Christian festival day?

283 Decorated with vine leaves and showing people drinking a cup of good cheer, what was first designed by Sir Henry Cole in 1843?

284 What is the name of the cake traditionally eaten on Mothering Sunday and on Easter Sunday?

285 Hallowe'en is based on ancient pagan religions but it is followed by the Christian festival of All Saints. When is the festival of All Saints celebrated?

286 Alms boxes, which were kept in churches, contained money donated for the poor. On what day were they traditionally opened and the money distributed?

287 What American holiday, celebrated with a dessert of pumpkin pie, recalls the story of how the 'Pilgrim Fathers' were helped by the local friendly Indians?

288 On what Christian festival day is Eucharist or Holy Communion never received?

289 In many European countries December 6th commemorates the patron saint of children. Who is this patron saint?

290 In some parts of the world 'Fat Tuesday' is a day of merrymaking and carnival. What is the name of the festival that means 'Fat Tuesday'?

FASTS AND FESTIVALS

291 First held in 1445 on Shrove Tuesday, what event happens every year in Olney, Buckinghamshire?

292 Who gives an Easter blessing known as 'Urbi et Orbi' which is broadcast around the world through radio and television?

293 While preaching the gospel Stephen was stoned to death. On what day of the year is St Stephen's Day?

294 Held on February 2nd, what festival celebrates the presentation of the infant Jesus in the temple?

295 Carnivals often take place before Lent. What does the word 'carnival' mean?

296 What Christian festival was traditionally marked by penance and fasting, until 1966 when the Pope declared that fasting was no longer a requirement?

297 Mardi Gras is a lively and joyous Christian festival. When exactly is it celebrated?

298 What is the special name given to the feast honouring the archangel Michael which takes place on September 29th?

299 Who was the tenth-century Bohemian king who was well known for his Christian love and compassion and who features in a well-known song sung at Christmas time?

300 What Christian festival takes place on the sixth Thursday after Easter and may involve the lifting of a statue of Jesus during a church service?

301 What is the name of the candle, used during a Christian festival, which is very large because it has to burn for forty days?

302 During what Christian festival would you expect to hear the Nativity story being read in a church service?

303 On the Thursday of Holy Week the altar cloth is traditionally removed from the altar. By what name is this festival day usually known?

304 Celebrated on February 2nd, what is the name of the festival that comes from the practice of blessing the supply of candles to be used in church during the year?

305 What is said to have been introduced into Christmas celebrations in Britain by Prince Albert in 1841 from his native Germany?

306 On what day do many churches hold a three-hour service from noon until 3 pm when worshippers meditate upon the crucifixion?

307 In Christianity when exactly is Holy Saturday?

308 What Christian festival day is often called the birthday of the Church?

309 In what Christian denomination might slava bread and dishes of boiled wheat be used to celebrate a saint's day?

310 What is the name of the special calendar used to count down the days to Christmas?

311 What is the name given to the Christian forty-day period of penance or fasting?

312 What Christian festival celebrates the coming of the Holy Spirit upon the disciples?

313 Christians celebrate the resurrection of Jesus on what special festival day?

314 On what day of the week is Pancake Day celebrated?

315 On what festival day do Christians remember the Last Supper and Jesus' commandment to love one another?

316 On what festival day in spring is the death of Jesus specially remembered?

317 Ten days before Whitsun or Pentecost, on what festival day is the paschal candle put out?

318 During which Christian festival might the words 'He came down to earth from heaven' be sung?

319 The Bible describes how Jesus' disciples were in a room in Jerusalem when suddenly they felt that they had the courage to go out and preach the Christian message. What Christian festival celebrates this event?

320 During what Christian festival might churches be decorated with a display of bread, fruit and vegetables?

QUESTIONS 311 – 320

321 During what winter festival might Christians place a decorated tree in their homes?

322 During Lent one day is set aside for thanking God for 'Mother' Church. By what name is it usually known today?

323 The spices in what festival food are said to be a reminder of the spices used in wrapping bodies before burial?

324 In the past, bishops, priests, popes and kings washed the feet of their subjects on what special day?

325 Called after a third-century saint, what is the name of the day in February on which it has become customary to send unsigned cards?

326 Traditionally given as a gift on Christmas Eve, what fruit is used to make a Christingle?

327 What autumn festival of thanksgiving for a good gathering of the crops is still celebrated in schools and churches today?

328 Often made into a wreath, what is the evergreen plant used at Christmas which has prickly leaves and red berries?

329 In Cyprus on Easter Sunday whose effigy is burnt on bonfires?

330 Although a public holiday in only a few countries, on what day of the week is Ascension Day always celebrated?

FASTS AND FESTIVALS

331 What do some Christians believe was unique and miraculous about Jesus' birth to Mary?

332 What is the name of the statement of belief, one version of which begins 'I believe in God, the Father Almighty, maker of heaven and earth, and in Jesus Christ, his only Son, our Lord …'?

333 Some Christians believe that there is a state after death which is for those not yet ready for heaven but not guilty of sins which condemn them to hell. What is it called?

334 In what branch of Christianity is there the belief that when the Pope speaks representing the Church he is without error or infallible?

335 What do Christians believe happened to Jesus three days after he was put to death?

336 What is the term for the belief that war under any circumstances is always wrong and should never be entered into?

337 A person who is quite certain that there is no God is called what?

338 Which day of the week do Christians believe is the 'Lord's Day' and a special day for worship and rest?

339 Condemned by the Roman Catholic Church and many other Christians as killing, what word describes the action of taking a person's life rather than letting them continue to suffer in pain?

340 'You shall not kill' and 'You shall not commit adultery' are the sixth and the seventh commandments. What is the fifth?

341 Thought by many to be morally wrong, what word describes the practice of experimenting on live animals?

342 Expressing his belief that there is a strong link between religion and politics, who said, 'I am puzzled about which Bible people are reading when they suggest religion and politics don't mix.'

343 In Christianity what is the dwelling place of God and the state of joy where the faithful enjoy the eternal blessing of God?

344 The belief that there is only one God is called what?

345 In the Roman Catholic Church if a person is canonized what do they become?

346 The 'paraclete' or the 'comforter' is a word used by Christians to refer to what?

347 What is the Hebrew word for 'the anointed one' or 'the Christ'?

348 The Parousia or eschatology refers to the belief in the second coming of whom?

349 Pride was the first, and believed to be the most dangerous, of the deadly sins listed by Pope Gregory the Great. How many deadly sins did Pope Gregory list?

350 Within Christianity there are three main statements of belief. The Nicene Creed and the Athanasian Creed are two of them. What is the third called?

351 Referred to in the statement of belief in the Church of England, who descended into hell and rose again on the third day?

352 Some Christians would call her Our Blessed Lady. Who are they talking about?

353 According to traditional Christian belief, which disciple was given the gift of the Keys of the Kingdom and stands at the gates into heaven?

354 According to Christian belief who said, 'I am the way and the truth and the life. No man comes to the Father but by Me'?

355 In Christianity what is the place of everlasting torment for the unjust and the unbelievers, a state of spiritual agony without the love of God?

356 What is the name given to the belief taught by John Calvin that God decides in advance a person's ultimate destiny?

357 What is the name given to the belief taught particularly within the Roman Catholic faith that bread and wine consecrated at the Eucharist or Mass truly become the body and blood of Christ?

358 What word describes speech or thought that expresses contempt for God?

359 Traditionally searched for by the Knights of the Round Table, what is the name of the goblet Jesus drank from at the last supper which has become a symbol of the Christian belief in a holy quest for the highest of ideals?

360 What is the name of the Christian sect that believes in keeping Saturday as the holy Sabbath?

BELIEFS

361 Some Christians believe that they should avoid eating red meat on what day of the week?

362 What name is given to the belief, held within the Roman Catholic Church, which claims that Mary the mother of Jesus was born without sin?

363 Many Christians call him Beelzebub. Who is Beelzebub?

364 According to some, there will be a final struggle or battle between good and evil before the Kingdom of God is fully established. What is this battle called?

365 In the teaching of the Roman Catholic Church what is the only thing that can dissolve a valid Christian marriage?

366 Who was imprisoned and threatened with torture by the religious authorities for his belief that the earth revolved around the sun?

367 In the Orthodox Church what is the name given to a sacred picture, usually of Jesus or a saint, which is painted on to treated wood?

368 Who would a Christian have in mind if he or she talked about the 'Lamb of God'?

369 A person who is uncertain about whether or not there is a God but is prepared to keep an open mind is called what?

370 In 1950 the Pope said that when this person died she 'was taken up, body and soul, into the glory of heaven'. Who was he talking about?

BELIEFS

ELIEFS

Quick Questions on Christianity

BELIEFS

371 'I believe in … the communion of saints, the forgiveness of sins, the resurrection of the body …': these are words from what?

372 What is the name given to the belief that there is a direct link between the sin of Adam and Eve and the sin of all humankind?

373 Name the belief that God is one in three.

374 Who do Christians believe is 'the Messiah'?

375 If a Christian described themselves as being a teetotaller what would they refuse to do?

376 Who do Christians believe suffered and died so that all humankind might be saved?

377 Christianity describes God as being omnipotent. What does omnipotent mean?

378 During what Christian ceremony is water used to symbolize the washing away of sin and being born again into a new life?

379 What branch of Christianity in 1968 gave its views on the subject of contraception in a document called *Humanae Vitae*?

380 Particularly in the Orthodox Church who is called the Theotokos, the God-bearer?

QUESTIONS 371 – 380

52

381 In traditional Christian belief what is the name given to the lord and leader of evil spirits who is the enemy of God?

382 What did Pope Pius XI call 'a very serious crime'?

383 From the Greek word for 'messenger', what is the name of the superhuman beings who some believe are God's heavenly helpers?

384 Whose theory of evolution, published in 1859, made many people question their belief that humans were descended from a single pair of ancestors?

385 Who do Christians believe will 'come again, with glory, to judge both the quick and the dead'?

386 Who is usually given the title 'the Madonna'?

387 In a 1976 declaration, what branch of Christianity claimed that during Mass the priest represents Jesus and that the role of Jesus must be taken by a man?

388 Who do Christians believe is the saviour and redeemer of all humankind?

389 What word describes an extraordinary event, such as the time when Jesus was said to have walked on water, believed to be caused by God?

390 Christians believe that marriage should be only between one woman and one man. What is this type of marriage called?

391 Many monks, nuns and priests believe in and practise celibacy. What does this involve?

392 The founder of the Sisters of Charity said, 'The greatest destroyer of peace in the world today is abortion'. Who was she?

393 In the play of the same name Doctor Faustus sold part of himself to the devil. What is the name for that part of a human being which is believed to survive bodily death?

394 Called after a precious metal, by what name is Jesus' rule 'Do to others as you would have them do to you' better known?

395 What word describes a false god or a statue of a false god, worship of which is forbidden according to the second commandment?

396 St Patrick, the patron saint of Ireland, is said to have used the shamrock as an aid to teaching about what Christian belief?

397 The belief that God should be seen as a liberator who opposes injustice and oppression is known as 'Liberation Theology'. In what part of the world did Liberation Theology develop?

398 Christianity has always rejected polytheism. What is polytheism?

399 In an Encyclical in 1988, what religious leader declared, 'The earth and all life on it is a gift from God given to us to share and develop, not to dominate and exploit'?

400 What branch of Christianity announced in 1660, 'We utterly deny all outward wars and strife and fightings with outward weapons ...'?

401 Who was the Archbishop of Canterbury who wrote the Book of Common Prayer and was later burnt at the stake in 1556?

402 Which Pope called for the Second Vatican Council in 1962 in order to update the Roman Catholic Church to meet the needs of the present day?

403 What organization was started in 1953 by the Christian priest Chad Varah to enable people who were depressed and suicidal to talk to someone by telephone?

404 What was the infamous Spanish investigation started in 1478 that tried to root out, often through torture and execution, people who were thought to be unbelievers or false Christians?

405 What branch of Christianity has a crest as a symbol with the words 'blood and fire' written on the design?

406 Who was the Christian missionary at 'The Inn of the Sixth Happiness' who in 1938 led a hundred Chinese children over mountains to safety from the Japanese army?

407 Motivated by his Christian faith, as a Member of Parliament David Alton attempted to introduce a law bringing tighter controls over what moral issue?

408 Who was the Christian doctor who, horrified at the number of children living on the streets of London, in 1870 set up the first of his many homes for homeless children?

409 Although officially withdrawn from the list of saints in 1969, who is still the patron saint of England?

410 What was the name of the German theologian who in 1913 gave up his studies to work as a doctor in Lambarene in West Africa?

411 Who was the Archbishop of Cape Town in South Africa who spoke out against apartheid?

412 Which German Christian minister who opposed Hitler was executed in Flossenburg concentration camp in 1945?

413 The Baptist missionary Stanley Browne went to Africa in 1936 and later pioneered ways of healing a disfiguring skin disease. What is the disease called?

414 Sometimes called 'The Father of the English Bible', who first translated the New Testament from Greek into English?

415 Who opened the 'Home for Dying Destitutes' in Calcutta?

416 Born in 1624, imprisoned six times and attacked by mobs, who was the founder of the Society of Friends (also known as the Quakers)?

417 What Christian Member of Parliament in 1885 campaigned for the introduction of Factory Acts in order to prevent young children from being exploited at work?

418 Who is usually said to be the first British Christian to have chosen death rather than give up his faith?

419 From 1738 until his death he preached all over England, started schools for the poor and founded the Methodist Church. Who was he?

420 Who was the former RAF bomber pilot who entered the Roman Catholic faith in 1948 and later opened homes for the sick?

421 In 1987 the Archbishop of Canterbury's special envoy was taken captive whilst negotiating the release of hostages in Beirut. Who was he?

422 Who was the non-violent American black leader who made a speech in 1963 known as 'I have a dream'?

423 Based in the Vatican in Rome, who is the head of the Roman Catholic Church?

424 In the nineteenth century William Booth started a branch of Christianity that has become well known for helping the elderly and poor. What is it called?

425 In 1989 two well-known singers sang together 'Whenever God shines His light'. Van Morrison was one. Who was the other?

426 Who was the Roman Emperor who declared in 312 CE that Christianity was a tolerated religion and who later summoned the Council of Nicaea?

427 Who resigned as Lord Chancellor and was beheaded in 1535 for refusing to sign an oath saying that King Henry VIII was the head of the Church and that Anne Boleyn was his true wife?

428 Born in 1493, who hung up his sword and founded the Society of Jesus (the Jesuits) which vigorously supported the Pope?

429 What is the name given to the movement within Christianity towards co-operation and eventual unity?

430 What was the famous book written by John Bunyan when he was in prison in the seventeenth century?

GENERAL

431 Some Christians wear a cross as a symbol of their faith. What other symbol, based on a Greek word, may they wear?

432 Which branch of the Christian Church regards the Pope as its leader?

433 What do the letters AD stand for?

434 What branch of Christianity has 'Thirty-Nine Articles of Faith' printed in the Book of Common Prayer?

435 What happened to many early Christians in the Coliseum in Rome?

436 Drawing upon her knowledge of pain control, what movement did Cicely Saunders establish?

437 Formed in 1964, what Christian charity aims to help those who are poor and hungry throughout the world?

438 What are the Greek letters alpha and omega sometimes used to mean?

439 What Church of England Bishop in 1993 said that he found it difficult to believe in the idea of eternal punishment in hell?

440 Glossolalia is sometimes experienced by Christians. What is it?

441 Who was the fourth-century North African bishop who wrote *Confessions* and *The City of God*?

442 By what name are the original twelve disciples of Jesus known?

443 By what name are members of the Church called who are not members of the clergy?

444 When a new Pope is elected the most important bishops in the Roman Catholic Church meet in secret conclave. What are these bishops called?

445 Sometimes described as early Protestants, the Lollards believed in a personal faith and the authority of the Bible and rejected the idea that a priest had to remain celibate. On whose teaching did they base their ideas?

446 Who was outraged by the sale of indulgences, was excommunicated from the Church in 1520 and was condemned at the Diet of Worms in 1521?

447 St Francis is said to have had visible wound marks in his hands, feet and side. What are these marks called?

448 What organization was set up in 1948 with the intention of bringing together Christians of different denominations so that they could discuss matters and work together?

449 Within the Roman Catholic Church the title 'the Vicar of Christ on Earth' refers to whom?

450 In the Anglican Church the Archbishop of Canterbury is the Primate of All England. Who is the Primate of England?

451 John Wesley founded a Christian denomination whose name is based upon its members' methodical practice of prayer and Bible study. What is it called?

452 Declared to be the 'Doctor of the Church', who was the thirteenth-century theologian whose *Summa Theologica* is one of the main descriptions of Roman Catholic theology?

453 What is the official Catholic Church agency that raises money and organizes relief and development schemes in countries in Africa, Asia and Latin America?

454 Who was the outspoken Archbishop of El Salvador who in 1980 was shot while celebrating Mass?

455 In C. S. Lewis' book *The Lion, the Witch and the Wardrobe*, based on a Christian theme, which character dies as a 'willing victim who has committed no treachery' and then returns to life in order that good may win the battle over evil?

456 Who was the Church of England monk who spoke against apartheid in South Africa in his 1956 book *Naught for Your Comfort?*

457 What word describes a method of instruction based on questions and answers which traditionally was used to prepare a person for Christian baptism?

458 Condemned for denying the doctrine of the Pope's supremacy, which English reformer has been called the 'Morning Star of the Reformation'?

459 Often called the 'Apostle of the Gentiles', who felt that he was called to preach Christianity to non-Jews?

460 On the nights of the 23rd and 24th August 1572 thousands of Huguenot Protestant Christians were slaughtered. What is this event called?

461 Who was the English shoemaker, born in 1761, who became a Baptist minister and early Protestant missionary to India?

462 Who was the first Christian Emperor of Rome, who claimed to see in the sky a fiery cross and the words 'By this sign conquer'?

463 There are three main branches in Christianity. Protestantism and Roman Catholicism are two. What is the third?

464 Born in Scotland in 1848, who was the woman who spent nearly forty years of her life working as a missionary in Africa and was known by the people she helped as 'the white ma'?

465 The first Roman Catholic President of the United States spoke publicly in support of civil rights. Who was he?

466 The Hollywood epic film *Quo Vadis?* has a scene that shows the crucifixion of which of Jesus' disciples?

467 Six of the seven deadly sins are pride, covetousness, lust, anger, gluttony and envy. What is the seventh?

468 What is the name given to the important act in the Roman Catholic Church by which the Pope declares that a person may be added to the list of saints?

469 Sponsored by the British Council of Churches, in what month is Christian Aid week held?

470 Supported by the Dutch Reformed Church but hated and opposed by many Christians, what was the name of the form of racial segregation introduced into South Africa in 1948?

471 A mitre is a special head-dress worn as a symbol of a person's office. Who would wear a mitre?

472 The General Synod in Britain meets two or three times a year. What branch of Christianity does it govern?

473 In Christianity monks traditionally shave off part of the hair on the head. What is this called?

474 Between 1618 and 1648 a religious and political war took place between European Catholic and Protestant countries. What is this war called?

475 Who said in 1994 that he would hope to be seen as 'Defender of the faiths'?

476 In Charles Dickens' story *A Christmas Carol* what was the name of the miser who discovered the spirit of Christmas?

477 Who believed that once when she was on a train in India God told her to give up being a teacher and instead work with the poor?

478 In the story from early Christianity, Androcles showed kindness towards what sort of animal?

479 The former Catholic priest Bruce Kent has spent many years campaigning against what?

480 Pope John Paul II was the first non-Italian Pope for 400 years. What nationality is he?

481 During a marriage service what object do couples often exchange as a sign of their love?

482 Women have been ministers in the URC since it began in 1972. What do the letters URC stand for?

483 Who in the New Testament said, '... the man who is guilty of sexual immorality sins against his own body. Don't you know that your body is the temple of the Holy Spirit ...'?

484 In the United Kingdom the number in 1961 was 27,000 and in 1993 180,000. Of concern to those who believe in marriage, what do these figures represent?

485 In order to humiliate and torture him before his death, what was said to have been placed on Jesus' head?

486 What BBC television programme, broadcast on Sundays, celebrated its 35th anniversary in 1996?

487 Condemned by some Christians as being immoral, in what year was abortion made legal in Britain?

488 In a church by what other name is the holy table usually known?

489 Who was the angel who announced to Mary that she would give birth to a special son?

490 The Son of God and the Holy Spirit are the second and third persons of the Trinity. Who is the first person of the Trinity?

491 Thought by some to be the holiest relic in Christianity, what is kept in the cathedral in Turin?

492 In what branch of Christianity are there five patriarchs, with a special position being given to the patriarch of Constantinople?

493 'Jesus is given his cross to carry' is one of the 'Stations of the Cross' often found around the walls of a church. How many stations are there?

494 Who in Christianity is described as being both fully God and fully human?

495 What film starring Harrison Ford has the hero living amongst the Christian Amish community in America?

496 Donald Coggan and Robert Runcie have both at one time held what position in the Church of England?

497 In 1948 a big step towards Church unity was taken when the WCC was formed. What is the WCC?

498 What is the name given to the circle of light often shown around a person's head to indicate holiness?

499 When using a rosary the worshipper says three different prayers. The Lord's Prayer and Gloria Patri are two of them. What is the third prayer?

500 A nineteenth-century religious leader who wanted to encourage worship through singing and music said, 'Why should the Devil have all the best tunes?'. Who was he?